D0259586

The Spot on My Bum

The Spot on My Bum

by *Gez Walsh*

Illustrations by Julie Thompson

The King's England Press

1997

The Spot on My Bum is typeset in 14pt Baskerville
and published by The King's England Press,
21 Commercial Road,
Goldthorpe Industrial Estate, Goldthorpe,
Rotherham, South Yorkshire, S63 9BL.

ISBN 1 872438 10 5

10th Impression, 1999

Printed and bound in Great Britain by Woolnough
Bookbinding Ltd, Irthlingborough, Northants

To my son, Lee Walsh.

Foreword

Spend half an hour with any gang of kids and you'll hear poems like Gez Walsh's. His work taps into that thick seam of comedy and rudeness that children love.

Poetry lovers might say that this isn't poetry, that snot, spot and poop jokes shouldn't be part of the gang that includes Shakespeare's *Sonnets* and Wordsworth's *Prelude*.

Well, I don't think Gez Walsh will mind too much about that: his poems are the voice of the playground, the voice of the top deck of the bus. They are part of that deep seated need for rhyme and rhythm that's in everybody, and part of the cheekiness that's kept us going since Adam was a lad.

So, onwards, poop, snot and spots!

Ian McMillan

The Spot on My Bum

Good grief! This spot on my bum,
I've squeezed it so much that my cheeks
Have gone numb.
It's big and it's red,
With a big yellow top,
I've squeezed it with pliers,
But still it won't pop!
I've soaked it in water,
I've put on some cream.
Mum had a squeeze,
Which just made me scream.
I can't sit down now,
The pain is quite dire,
My spot is glowing,
And my bum is on fire!
I cried to my mum
"Just one last try, please."
So mum, with a grip like Superman,
Started to squeeze.
Yes, mum had hold of my spot,
With a vice-like grip.
My eyes they were popping
And I was biting my lip.
My body started shaking without restraint,
My legs they wobbled,
I started to faint.
Then my mum cried out with such distaste,
Because my spot, like a time-bomb,
Had exploded in her face!

Grandad Pruning

Grandad was asleep
In his rocking chair,
When I noticed from his nose was hanging
One long ,black hair.
The poor old man was in a deep sleep,
So up to his chair I did creep.
His mouth was open,
His face was a blank,
So I took hold of the hair,
And gave it a yank.
Grandad he screamed,
And grabbed hold of his nose.
As the pain shot through his body,
He curled up his toes.
Grandad he said, "What on earth do
You think you're doing?"
I said "It's alright, I'm just Grandad pruning!"

Bath-time Trouble

I was sat in the bath,
Having a laugh,
When I got myself into trouble.
I was just sat there without a care,
Breaking wind and making bubbles.
But there was just one thing

That I wanted to know,
That was, up the cold tap could I fit my big toe?
So I pushed it up with all my might,
And my toe went up,
Although it was tight.
At first I was pleased,
But then I started to shout.
My foot turned blue,
And my toe wouldn't come back out.
Mum came running into the bathroom,
Saying, "Why are you shouting like that?
All the neighbours can hear you,
And why is your toe up the tap?"
I cried, "Mum please help me,
My toe is stuck fast."
So she twisted and pulled it,
Then finally she gasped,
"I'll go get your father
And see what he says,
I'll be gone just a minute,
So don't go away."
So a minute later,
Mum came back with dad,
His face was turning red,
I think he was mad.
Dad just shook his head,
And called me a fool,
Then he went out to the garage,
To get his tools.
My sister walked in and started to laugh.
I tried to cover myself up,
As mum drained the water out of the bath.

Mum gave me a towel,
To put over my willy,
Dad took the tap off the bath,
I really felt so silly.
So off we went to the hospital,
To have the tap removed.
I walked into the waiting room,
Wearing one tap and one shoe.
I hobbled over and sat in a chair,
Trying hard to ignore all the people,
Who laughed as they stared.
An old man leaned over and whispered,
"I hope you don't mind me asking,
But I can see you've been doing
A spot of tap dancing!"
And the nurse couldn't stop laughing,
As she cut the tap off and set me free.
Mum said, "Let this be a lesson."
In future it's a shower for me.

Dad's Pad

My dad says that I'm a bad lad.
He's mad that I had his pad.
It's sad that a writing pad
Could make a grown-up so mad.
But that's my dad, another fad.
I suppose I should be glad
That my dad's fad is not as sad
As some sad dads' bad fads that can be had.

My sister Bec

My sister Rebecca is a real smarty.
She beats up all the boys,
Because she's a black belt in karate.
She can ride a horse,
She can climb a tree,
And when she's around,
No one picks on me.
She is so good looking,
With long blonde hair,
And what people think of her,
She just doesn't care.
But there's just one problem
With our Bec,
And that's I have to live with her,
And she's a pain in the neck!

Girlfriend

I can't believe it happened,
It's such a disgrace,
I went to kiss my girlfriend,
And I burped in her face.
She was so disgusted at what I had just done,
That she's no longer my girlfriend,
And she's going to tell my mum.
But I really don't know
What all the fuss is about,
Because burping is not such a crime.
And anyway she can tell my mum,
Because mum keeps burping all the time.

The Accident

Psst, I'm in here,
I'm hiding from my mum,
Because it's only a matter of time,
Before she finds out what I've done.
I have to keep my voice down,
In case she might hear.
The thought of her finding me
Fills me with fear.
It was an accident you see,
Oh why do these things always happen to me?
Aaargh!! Oh no, she's seen it,

14

There's no mistaking that,
She's seen the fridge door,
Where I've super-glued the cat.

Train Journey

"Just get on the train,
Get on the train
And stop your moaning,
You're always the same,
Always the same.
Now go and sit down,
Just take a seat,
And I'll go to the buffet car
And get something to eat.
Would you like ham,
Or maybe some cheese?"
"Nothing for me, just a drink please."
"Oh look, we're moving."
"How long will it take?"
"Oh stop your moaning for heaven's sake."
"I don't like trains. I don't like trains."
"What did you say? What did you say?"
"Why do we have to catch a train anyway?"
"Just look out the window and see the sights.
Oh look, there's a tunnel,
On go the lights."
"Why has it gone dark? I don't like the dark."
"Look just stop your moaning,
Don't be such a nark.
Look, here we are at the tunnel end
And I can see a big bridge just around the bend."
"Oh no, what if it's broken
And we cannot stop,

And the train crashes into the water with a mighty plop?"
"But the bridge is so strong,
It's been there for so long,
Nothing can go wrong,
Nothing can go wrong.
Oh, look over there,
I can see the sea.
We are coming to the end of our journey.
Look, the train is slowing
And starting to stop
And people are standing,
It's time to get off."
"Oh, I just can't wait to get off this train.
I'm sorry for nagging,
And for being such a pain.
I promise you next time mum,
I won't make such a fuss,
If you promise me next time we can catch the bus."

Can I Go to the Toilet?

"Please miss, can I go to the toilet?"
"No, you should have gone at play time."
"Please miss, can I go to the toilet?"
"No, just do your sums."
"Please miss, can I go to the toilet?"
"No, you shouldn't have drunk so much."
"Please miss, CAN I GO TO THE TOILET?"
"No, you will have to learn to control yourself."
"Please miss, er, can I change my trousers?"

It's Not Fair

Aw mum, it's not fair,
I always get blamed
When things go wrong
Which really makes me mad.
Well, okay, I admit to painting the dog red,
But surely that doesn't make me bad?
And I got blamed for the toilet seat
That was spread with gum
When I was as innocent as anyone.
Though I must admit I laughed quite a bit
When your knickers got stuck to your bum.
But I'll tell you what really makes me see red
Is you blaming me for our gerbil being dead.
Just how do you think that makes me feel?
It was because he was weak-hearted
That now he's departed,
Not because I kept spinning his wheel!

A Day at the Seaside

I went to the seaside with my Grandad
And the sun it was really beating down,
Which really makes me glad.
My Grandad, he hired a deck chair

And sat out on the sands.
Me, I had an ice cream
That dribbled down my hand.
I said to Grandad,
"You should cover up your bald head,"
'Cos he was looking like a raspberry,
He was turning really red.
But Grandad didn't listen,
Until we were about to go.
His little bald head was shining,
It really had a glow.
He should have put his hat on sooner,
To cover his glowing skull,
Because he went and got it splattered
With bird muck from a passing gull.

The Smell from Under the Bed

There's a disgusting smell
Coming from under my bed,
And I'm scared to look
In case I find something that's dead.
The smell has been getting worse
Throughout the week,
I can't stand it no more,
I'll have to take a peek.
What will I find?
I dread to think.
What on earth could make such a stink?
To let in some air,
I opened the door.
I took a deep breath,
And laid down on the floor.
Then what a relief
When I moved back my books,
It's not a dead body,
But my old sweaty socks!

My Grandad

Have you met my Grandad?
He's got bad breath
And stinky feet.
He picks his nose
And he dribbles when he eats.
He's got a lovely big, toothless smile,
And he poops when he's in bed.
But to my Grandad
I'm a special little girl,
And to me he's the best Grandad
In the whole wide world.

Our New Baby

My mum has had a baby
A couple of days ago.
And why the heck she loves him
I really will never know.
He's all pink and wrinkly,
With crusty snot around his nose,
Mum she says, "Sit and hold your brother,
But he just lays there
Burping and gurgling,
Whilst poohing in his clothes.
Mum said, "Don't you think he's lovely?"
Just as he was sick down the front of my shirt.
But I don't think he's lovely,
He's just a troublesome little berk!

Clean Up Your Room

My mum says I'm old now, old enough
To do things for myself.
She wants me to clean my room up,
And tidy up my shelves.
I think that she's being selfish,
That's always been her job you see,
It's just because she's getting lazy,
That she's trying to pass her jobs on to me.
I've told her to see her doctor,
It's urgent help she must seek.
You see this is not a one-off,
She wants me to clean up once a week.
The work would take me hours,
To make me do this would be a sin.
And I'm sure you would be on my side,
If you saw the state that my room gets in.

The Berk

I dun't need to go to t' skool,
Coz I'm brainy enoof ya see.
Them teechers can't tell me nowt,
Coz I've got a brain the size of a planet, me.
I'll just stay at home
And watch telly,
That will learn me more,
Coz I fink reeding books and fings
Are really just one big bore.
And wen all t'other kidz have grown up,
They will have to take eggzams,
And wen they pass em,
Their future they will ave t'plan.
Some will go to t' university,
And some will go to t'work,
But me I'll still be sat here watching telly
Coz I'm not such a berk.

Grandma's Jumper

My Grandma has knitted me a jumper.
She said, "It's just a bit big for you,
But you're still growing."
But I don't think it would fit me,
Even if I weighed sixteen stones.
The neck hangs over my shoulders
And my hands don't come out of the bottom of the sleeves.
And the bottom of the jumper,
Hangs six inches below my knees,
But I didn't want to upset Grandma
So I told her it was nice,
And I wear it when I visit her,
That's why this year I've only seen her twice.

Fighting

Mum is going to kill me when I get home tonight,
'Cos I've gone and ripped my best coat
And I ripped it in a fight.
My mum she doesn't like fighting,
She thinks it's really bad,
But I think she might be good at it,
Because she really scares my dad.
Sometimes she gets angry with him,
And pokes him in the chest,
And then she tells him to shut up,
If he knows what's for the best.
My dad, he just smiles,
Then gives a little shrug.
My mum, she just goes storming off,
I think she might be a thug!

The Swimming Pool

I got kicked out of the swimming baths,
For acting like a fool.
I was standing on the diving board,
And weeing in the pool.
I was such a disgusting child,
The swimming baths man said,
Because I didn't look below me,
And I was weeing on Fred's head.

Brussels Sprouts

I would fight a pack of lions,
I would climb a mountain high,
I would jump out of an aeroplane
And fly down through the sky.
I would swim in a pool of alligators,
Or a shark infested sea,
But there's no way I'll eat brussels sprouts
When we have them for tea.

My Dog's Got Three Legs

My dog's got three legs
Cos he's had one cut off.
I asked him how he felt,
He just looked at me and said "Ruff!"
I used to walk him with my dad sometimes after dark,
But now he doesn't walk that good
So we take him for a drag in the local park.
But I still love my dog,
Although he's not the same.
You see we used to call him Sprinter,
But now he'd look a fool:
So because he's got three legs
We decided to call him Stool!

The Demon Barber

My mum she says,
"Why do you always misbehave?"
But I can't see what all the fuss is about.
I only gave the dog a shave,
The dog didn't seem to mind,
Though he now looks a little weird.
I used my dad's electric razor,
With which he trims his beard.
My mum says that the blades are ruined
And that the batteries have gone flat.
You know it's funny she should say that,
Because that's exactly what happened,
When I shaved Harry the cat.

Itsy Bitsy Spider

Itsy bitsy spider climbed up the water spout,
So I turned on the tap,
And I washed the spider out.
But that dumb spider
Climbed up the spout again,
And when he came out into my bath tub,
I squashed him, what a pain.

Monsters in My Room

Does your bedroom have monsters,
That come out late at night?
And does your wall-paper have faces,
Which appear when your mum turns out the light?
And from your wardrobe can you hear whispers,
A strange silent kind of noise?
But the scariest of all,
Are the faces of your toys.
But when you put the light on
Do the monsters go away?
Is the wall-paper just wall-paper
And do the noises have no more to say?
The reason that things are different,
I am sure that you will find,
Is when you realise they were never there,
They were always just in your mind.

Where's my specs?

"Where's my specs?"
My Dad did shout.
"If you've been messing with them
You won't be playing out."
I just could not believe
What he had just said,
Because the stupid berk had them
On the top of his head!

Look After Your Teeth

I had to go to the dentist today,
Mum says that I eat too many sweets,
Which has caused me to have tooth decay.
When I was sat in the dentist's waiting for them to call my name,
I was shaking with fear
And my tooth was in pain.
The reception lady said,
"Don't worry, you'll be fine."
But then she would say that, wouldn't she
Because he's not going to drill her teeth,
He's going to drill mine.
Then I heard the words
Which filled me with fear,
"He's ready for you now,
Can you just come through here."
As I walked into the dentist's lair,
My legs started shaking as I caught sight of the chair.
The dentist he said, "Climb into the chair
And open your mouth wide.
I won't be a second, then I'll have a look inside."
So the dentist leaned over and looked in my mouth.
He said "Ah, it's the back tooth that's the problem,
I'm afraid it will have to come out."
The dentist moved in closer,
I could smell his bad breath.
He picked up a needle

Which scared me to death.
He said, "Don't worry, you won't feel a thing."
I wondered if he would say that,
If I was sticking it in him.
As the needle went into my gums,
I felt a sharp prick.
A lump came to my throat,
I started to feel sick.
Then I had to wait a few minutes
For my mouth to go numb.
Then my teeth started to itch
And I couldn't feel my tongue.
The dentist put a clamp on my tooth,
And gave it a pull.
I grabbed hold of the chair
And took a big gulp.
Then the dentist smiled and said
"That's it, all done.
Now rinse out your mouth to clean up your gums."
So I rinsed out my mouth,
Into the sink,
With a funny tasting liquid,
Which was a deep shade of pink.
So that was it,
Everything all done.
I walked out with spit on my chin
And my face all numb.
So let this be a warning to all you kids out there,
Don't eat too much chocolate,
And of your teeth take care!

The Class 6 Army Song

I haven't learned a single thing,
Since our poor teacher went missing.
She got herself in such a fix,
Because she had to teach crazy class 6.
She said class 6 have driven her barmy,
So she ran away to join the army.
Now her sergeant major is really rough,
But compared to class 6 he's not that tough.
So, until we get another teacher,
What we're going to say will just not please you.
We'll scream and shout and mess about all day long.

What Are They?

What has eyes
But cannot see?
You sometimes have them round for tea.
Some are kings,
But they have no thrones,
They all lay in beds,
But they have no homes.
They all have jackets,
But with no buttons or zips,
And on a cold winter's night,
Be careful, they might burn your lips.
What are they?

Answer - Potatoes

An Apple For Lunch

While eating an apple at school today,
I was just chilling out,
Watching the other kids play.
The apple was so big, red and sweet,
I thought to myself it was good of mum,
To give me such a treat.
But then, with the last bite of the apple,
I started to squirm,
Because that's when I noticed a HALF EATEN WORM!

My Friend Tim

From my nose I've picked a big, green bogey
And I'm going to call him Tim.
So I think I'll stick him underneath my desk,
Where no one else can find him.
And when the school bell rings,
And it's time to go back home,
I think I'll stick him back up my nose
So he'll never be alone!

Has Anyone seen Freddy?

Has anyone seen Freddy, my frog?
I wish I knew where he had gone.
He's green, with funny eyes,
And he's about ten centimetres long.
He croaks as he hops around on skinny legs so long.
He also catches flies with his sticky tongue.
Oh, I hope that he is found,
And that he's found soon.
Because last time that I lost him
My mum found him in her bedroom.
And I can tell you that when she found him
She gave out such a shout,
Because she had just pulled up her undies,
When Freddy popped out!

Teeth

My teacher, Beaky Bamforth,
Has very strange teeth:
They flap up and down,
When he talks and he breathes.
But his are not the strangest
Teeth that I have seen,
Not by far,
Because my Grandad's teeth, they grin at me,
From the inside of a jar!

The Monster on the Stairs

There is a monster on our staircase,
Which no one else can see.
It's big, with red eyes and pointy teeth,
And it just sits there waiting for me!
I don't know why no one else can see it,
They just don't believe that it's there.
But I know it's waiting to trap me
At the top of the stairs.
The other day it nearly caught me,
I was trapped, frozen with fright.
But my dad came and scared it away,
By switching on the landing light.
My mum and dad say that I am silly,
But I really don't care.
And I'll tell you that there's no way that I'm going to bed alone,
Because I know that monster's there.

Two Little Kittens

Two little kittens, playing in some hay.
One of them pooped, so the other did say,
"What's that smell, and from where did it come?"
The first one laughed then said,
"I'm not so sure, but I think it was my bum."
The second one said, "Oh dear, is there something wrong
For your bum to make such a terrible pong?"
The first one said "I'll be just fine.
It's just that since I ate my tea,
My bum keeps exploding from time to time."

Soup

Slippy, sloppy, slimy soup,
Just add curry powder
To make you poop:
Add some spuds to make it thick,
and a drop of custard to make you sick.
Add some beans,
Then a few beans more,
And you won't stop pooping,
Until your bum gets sore!

Evander Prowse

An evil old man named Evander Prowse,
Hated visitors at his house.
So one day this evil old man
Decided to rid himself of visitors
With an evil plan.
He said "To rid myself of people, I know what I'll do.
I"ll cook them all a meal that tastes like pooh!"
So he sent out invitations to all around,
That said the most sumptuous meal that can be found.
Be here at 8.30 at my house,
Yours sincerely, Evander Prowse."
So he set about making his revolting meal.
He filled a pan of water,
And put in two conger eels.
Then he added two pounds of mustard,
The nose of an aardvark and two gallons of custard.
And from his garden he put in some in some lillies,
And to add a bit of spice,
Three pounds of chillies.
Evander had a taste from the pot which made him feel sick.
"That's perfect," he said. "This should do the trick."
And as for the puddings, they were round and flat.
They smelled disgusting; they were custard cow pats.
So at half past eight, when his guests arrived,
He smiled and said, "Please do come inside."
He said, "Please sit at the table, the meal won't be long.
The guests looked at each other
Because the room was filled with a terrible pong.

Evander put on some very loud music,
Just to get them in the mood.
But the guests all looked nervous,
When they realised that the pong was the food.
Evander served out the food in wooden bowls,
Great big dollops of aardvark's nose.
The guests took a mouthful and could take no more.
Clutching their stomachs, they ran for the door.
Evander danced as he laughed, "Oh, what a good plan."
A disgusting meal from a disgusting old man.
But that stupid old Evander didn't know his plan had failed,
Because his guests all got together and loudly wailed:
"Poor old Evander, just look at the food he eats.
No proper vegetables, no proper meats."
So from that night Evander was alone no more,
Because every evening there was a queue at his door.
The people would shout "Poor old Evander,
Come and eat at our house."
So the plan had backfired on that evil old Evander Prowse.

The Elephant and The Lion

An elephant out walking in the jungle alone,
He felt so tired, but he was so far from home.
His legs ached so much, he was in need of a rest.
He thought, "I think I'll lie down a while,
Yes I think that will be best."
So he found a place for safe keeping,
But he didn't notice below him, a lion that was sleeping.
So the elephant sat down, and with his huge behind,
Squashed the lion into the ground.
What the elephant didn't know
Was that he'd just used as a mat
The king of the jungle,
A big, dangerous cat.
The lion he gasped, "Get off me, you lump."
But the elephant couldn't hear him,
Because he was busy examining his trunk.
The elephant, now relaxed, thought of a tune that he did know.
He thought, "Oh, what was it now, and how does it go?"
But the lion beneath him was fast losing breath,
And if he didn't do something soon he'd be smothered to death.
The elephant, meanwhile, was still unaware
That squashed beneath his bum the lion was there.
Then the tune came to him, and he started to hum,
But soon let out a scream as the lion bit his bum.
As the elephant jumped around, waving his bum in the air,
The lion roared "You stupid lump, didn't you see me laid
                                                    there?"
But the elephant just cried, saying, "There was no need for that."
The lion replied, "Well maybe in future you'll look below you,
And not use a lion as a mat."

Vera Jaffing

There was once a young woman called Vera Jaffing,
Who, try as she might, she just couldn't stop laughing.
She would walk around the streets with tears in her eyes,
Laughing at people as they passed her by.
But then one day, while she was out walking,
She started to laugh at two old ladies as they were talking.
One old lady thought this was shocking.
She said to Vera "Why are you laughing,
And who do you think you're mocking?"
This made Vera just laugh more,
In fact she laughed so much that she wet her drawers.
The old lady waved her stick at Vera and started to roar
"You stupid girl, now just shut up."
But as she stepped forward, she tripped and fell on the floor.
Soon people started to gather round.
What a sight! Vera laughing like a banshee
And the old lady spread-eagled on the ground.
The people said to Vera "Look,
The old lady's hurt, so how on earth can you snigger?"
Vera replied "Don't you find it funny,
Look, she's showing her knickers!"
Then the police arrived,
Because the people had begun to scream and shout.
They pointed at Vera and said,

"There she is, now sort her out!"
So the police took Vera down to the station.
People screaming, Vera laughing,
The old lady still spread-eagled, what a strange situation.
The police took Vera to see their sergeant.
They told him that Vera's laughing
Had caused a great argument.
The sergeant shook his head and said
"Tomorrow you'll have to appear in court.
Now take her away and lock her up,
While I make out my report."
So at nine thirty the next morning,
Vera was stood alone in the dock.
She was laughing at a fat lady in a pink, flowery frock.
Then the judge arrived and sat in a chair
That looked comfortable but big.
Vera burst out laughing. She shouted,
"Look, that man's wearing a wig!"
The judge shouted "Order, order,
Or you'll be in contempt of court."
Vera laughed, "You can take my order,
I'll have a very large port."
"That's it," said the judge.
"Take her away and lock her up.
That will stop her laughing, the cheeky young pup."

So that was it. Vera's now doing time.
She didn't know that laughing was such a great crime.
But the one thing that Vera learned while she was in prison,
Is that there's a time to laugh, and a time to listen!

Big Bertha

There's a woman who lives down our street,
And she's the biggest woman that you will ever, ever, meet.
She must be about seven feet tall,
And weigh at least sixteen stones.
The other day she shouted at her cat,
And the whole neighbourhood ran in home.
Although we call her big Bertha,
Her real name is Claire,
And if she stands still long enough
Birds nest in her hair.
And when her dresses get too tight,
Or when thy're old and spent,
She gives them all to Oxfam,
Who sell them on as tents.
To me she is so scary, especially when she's cross,
Because her face reminds me of a bulldog,
Chewing a big fat wasp!
She makes her husband's life a misery,
The poor man is very small.
The other day she shouted at him, "Kiss me!"
And so he could do this she picked him up,
And stood him on the garden wall.
But then I'm sure that he loves Bertha,
And that's a very good thing.
But I'd like to tell you all now,
That I'm glad I'm not him!

Little Green Germ

A little green germ,
Floating in the air,
He flew up my nose
And decided to settle himself there.
Then after a while, he thought he'd have some fun.
So he made my eyes water,
And caused my nose to run.
But I wasn't prepared to put up with such a lout,
So I went aaachoo!
And sneezed the lout out.

To the Doctor's

I had to go to the doctor's
Because I wasn't feeling well.
Every time I pooped I poohed,
And my room began to smell.
The doctor said, "Come over here
And don't be frightened, son."
Then he asked me what the problem was,
I said it was my bum.
He said "Just take these tablets,
And you'll soon be feeling fine."
I hope to heck that he is right
Cos I keep pooping all the time.

Grandad in Space

Grandad nearly gave us all a heart attack,
The day he had a fart attack.
It all started one afternoon,
When a strange eggy smell filled the room.
We were all gasping for air by half past three,
But he just kept on farting,
Right through "Neighbours" and while eating his tea.
That was it, we could take no more,
We opened all the windows
And we opened all the doors.
I said "It's no good mum, we'll have to move him,
He's been eating baked beans."
There was no way we could stop him now,
He had turned into a rampant farting machine.
So we all pushed Grandad outside in his wheelchair,
But his farts were getting stronger,
They were now lifting him in the air.
So we all held him down,
Just to make sure that he didn't take off.
But the smell was so bad,
That we started to splutter and cough.
But Grandad knew how to sort things out.

He took his tobacco and filled his pipe,
Then he got his matches to set it alight.
My dad shouted "No, don't strike that match!"
But it was too late, he did it,
And all we could do was stand back and watch.

The match ignited Grandad's fart,
With such a ferocious pace,
That it blew him out of his wheelchair
And deep into uncharted space.
A passing space shuttle saw him from their control room.
They said, "Mission control, we have a problem.
We've just seen an old man with a pipe,
Orbiting the moon."
Grandad saw the space shuttle, he waved at them.
"Hello!" he yelled, then headed back for earth again,
Still fart-propelled.
He was soon through the atmosphere,
He was now all steamy and wet.
Then he turned his bum to the ground
And hovered, just like a Harrier Jump Jet.
Grandad descended to earth,
With elegance and grace.
His gas was now running out,
But he still had a cheeky smile upon his face.
So that was it, his big adventure was over,
Although his wheelchair was now blown apart.
But I'm proud to have a Grandad
Who had travelled the galaxy,
Propelled by a fart.

The Cowboy Family

There was once a cowboy called
Six Gun Den,
Who rode a horse called
Big Bum Ben.
And he had a wife called
Big Nose Lil,
And a little son called
Spotty Face Will.
And they all lived in a shack
At Deadman's Creek,
But they had only moved there
Late last week.
Because until then
Six Gun Den was Builder Len,
Big Nose Lil was Dinner Lady Jill,
And Spotty Face Will was, well,
Spotty Face Will,
And they didn't all live in a wild west shack,
They lived in a council house in Huddersfield,
Which had a swing round the back.

Charlie Cheep

Charlie Cheep, a cheeky chap,
Carried a chicken, clucking and crowing in a sack.
Children complained about cheeky Charlie's cruelty,
But cheeky Charlie Cheep, with a cheesy grin,
Would not release that clucking and crowing chicken.
But one day when cheeky Charlie Cheep,
A cheeky chap, shut his eyes to have a nap,
The caring but cheeky children chose to release
The clucking and crowing chicken from the sack.
Once released from that dingy bag
The chicken's face was no longer sad.
First the chicken clucked, then it crowed,
And the children cheered, and then they roared,
To see cheeky Charlie Cheep without his cheesy grin,
Chasing his clucking and crowing chicken
Around his cluttered kitchen.

Spaceman

I know a little man
Who came from outer space.
He has a fried egg upon his head,
And a rasher of bacon upon his face.
He has a big pot belly,
And flippers instead of feet,
And he always blows a raspberry
To everyone he meets.

My Dream

The other night in my dreams
I was walking down a road,
When I bumped into a policeman,
Who then turned into a toad.
It was then I saw my teacher,
Her name is Miss McGluck,
She had a big orange bill upon her face,
She had turned into a duck.
And as she waddled past me
I saw feathers on her back.
I called out her name,
But she turned to me and just said, "Quack".
So I carried on walking
Until I arrived back at my house.
But, as I opened my front door,
I was amazed at what I saw,
Because mum turned into a cat,
And my dad turned into a mouse,
Then mum chased dad round the kitchen floor.
That was when I woke up,
It was just too weird,
And I couldn't take any more.

Climbing Trees

As I climbed up a big oak tree,
To see if I could get up to the top,
All my friends stood below,
Shouting for me to stop.
I shouted down to them,
"Don't worry, I'm not going to slip,
I've climbed up here many times
And I've a very strong grip."
But now I wish that I had listened
To what they said,
Because I wouldn't be here in hospital,
With my broken leg.

I Want to Poop

I want to poop,
But it's so rude
Because people are eating,
And they would say that I am crude.
I know as I poop I'll cough as well,
Then people won't hear from me;
But then I'm forgetting the eggy smell.
I know what to do,
It's just the job,
I'll just break wind
And I'll blame the dog.

Cowpat Boots

I was out walking in the countryside
With my new all-weather rucksack,
When I slipped upon a cowpat
And fell down on my back.
I quickly got back to my feet
And wiped off that stinky cowpat,
When out of the corner of my eye
I saw a cow passing by.
So I shouted, "Oi, did you do that?"
The cow just looked at me,
All innocent and dumb,
But I knew it had put that cowpat there,
Because I could see that it hadn't wiped its bum.

Dorothy Trip

Dorothy Trip had such enormous lips
That they dragged along the floor.
She was in such a fix,
With her huge rubber lips
That once she caught them in a door.
So it's sad to say,
But with all the other kids she could not play,
Because her huge rubber lips always got in the way.

But one day, just by mistake,
Dorothy did something that the other kids thought was great.
While they were on a school outing,
Dorothy tripped over her lips,
Fell off a bridge and started shouting.
And as her mouth opened wide,
Her lips like a suction cup stuck to the side.
The other kids screamed, "Miss, just look at Trip,
She's bungee jumping using her lips!"
Teacher shouted, "Trip, you fool!"
But as Dorothy bounced up and down,
The kids said "Cool!"
So now everyone is friends with Dorothy Trip,
The little girl with the amazing bungee jumping lips.

Cock a doodle doo

I woke up one morning,
To the sound of a cockerel call.
I could see it through my window,
It was standing on a wall.
He was stood there crowing,
"Cock a doodle doo!"
I shouted out, "Shut up,
Or I'll cock a doodle you!"
But that cockerel just let out another call;
That was when the boot I threw,
Knocked it off the wall.

The Super Hero

Once a young boy,
No different to any other.
He played football with his mates
And got picked on by his brother.
But one day,
He was hiding in the attic,
When he found a tea chest,
Containing an old vest
And a cloak-like jacket.
So he wrapped them up
And got down from the loft,
And went into his bedroom,
To see what he had got.
Now what they really were
Heaven only knows,
But this young boy was convinced
That they were super hero clothes.
So he put them on,
Thinking he looked cute,
But he needed something to finish
Off his super hero suit.
"I know what I need," he said,

"To make this suit just right."
So he sneaked into his mother's bedroom
And took her black tights.
So he put on the tights
And some undies on top,
Then the vest and cloak,
Wow, did he look a clot!
He thought "I'm no longer a mild mannered boy called Virgil,
I'm a super hero, I'm Super Gerbil!"
So he bounded downstairs,
Faster than a speeding marble.
He burst into the kitchen
And fell over the table.
Super Gerbil, with his wrinkly tights,
Looked such a prat,
As he fell off the table
And squashed the cat.
He got to his feet,
Trying to look cool,
His mum she screamed,
"Get upstairs now.
And take those tights off, you stupid fool."
So that was the end of Super Gerbil.
With his cloak across his back,
He was hiding in the loft again,
In case he got a smack!

Gemma

My name's Gemma
And I'm really clever
I'm the envy of all the other girls
I don't wear skirts
Or shoes that hurt
And I don't wear my hair in curls
The reason for their envy
Is very plain to see
It's because I'm good at football
And the boys all call for me!

Chewing Gum

I have swallowed my chewing gum
Which gave me such a fright
Because I think that in my belly
A bubble will grow tonight
It will grow so big
And just will not stop
That by the morning
I'll just go "Pop!"

Auntie Joan

I have to visit my Auntie Joan.
I don't really like her because she smells of sweaty socks,
And all she does is moan.
And I don't think that she washes herself for weeks,
Months, or even years,
Because if you get up close to her
You can see pools of rippling wax in her ears.
She once cooked me a meal,
It looked like snotty snails,
and when she passed me the plate,
I noticed her black finger nails.
But Joan doesn't care what people think or say,
She says it's her life and she chooses to live it that way.
I suppose she's right to choose a life that's not hectic,
But can you understand why I call her
My Auntie Septic!

Mad Beefburgers

I can no longer eat beefburgers,
Because some cows have gone mad.
My mum says that if I want to eat beef,
For my health it would be bad.
I suppose there must be some truth
In what my mother says,
Because she's always eaten beef,
And she's very strange in her ways.

Orders

Mum she shouts, "Get down out of that tree.
If you break your legs don't come running to me."
She says, "Sit up straight, and eat with your mouth closed."
So where do I put my food, up my nose?
She says, "Shut your eyes and go to sleep,
Wash your face and clean your teeth.
Eat your dinner, don't leave your greens,
And what's that stain down your jeans?"
All these orders are driving me barmy,
I think mum should be a sergeant in the army.

My Spider

There is a big black spider,
That hangs above my bed,
And every night when I go to sleep,
He swings above my head.
But he doesn't scare me,
As I stare at him out of the corner of my eye.
He would only bother me if I was a little hairy fly.
For then he would swoop down,
And wrap me in his web,
And suck out all my juices,
And leave me trussed up and dead.
But I still like him,
No matter what he eats.
He can keep his hairy old flies,
And I'll keep eating sweets.

The Bar 'B' Cue

Last night we had a bar'b'cue,
We had it round the back,
Dad put some meat upon the grill,
Then waited for it to go black.
But the food just would not cook,
Dad said, "I don't think it's yet alight"
Then he threw on some lighter fuel,
Which gave us all a fright.
The fuel blew up the barbecue,
Sending it spinning in the air,
Dad was stood with a burger on his head,
And it blew Grandma out of her chair.
So instead of eating spicy foods,
From many different lands,
We ended up with a takeaway,
That we bought from Greasy Anne's!

Chips, Chips, Chips

I want chips for my breakfast,
Chips for lunch,
Chips for dinner,
Chips for supper,
Just give me chips,
And a lovely hot cuppa,
Because I don't like fruit,
And I don't like veg,
I would rather eat our front hedge,
So no other food will pass my lips,
Just give me a cup of tea,
And a nice bag of chips.

My Name Is

Oh, I wish I was called Lynne,
Or Gemma or Lucy.
Any name would do,
I'm really not that choosy.
They could call me Charlotte,
Or Emma or Jane.
In fact they could call me anything,
Please just give me another name.
Yes, Mum could have named me
By lots of names,
From Kirsty to Annie,
But she went and named me after Grandma,
She went and named me Fanny!

Lee for England

It's 3 p.m. and the whistle blows,
But our striker is stood blowing his nose,
The ball whistles past him
With great pace,
So our defender rushes forward,
But trips over his lace;
Then the goalie comes out,
He will save it, you bet,
But the ball bounced off his head,
And landed in the net.
We're going to lose,
That's plain to see,
But then on to the field
Walks "Super Lee"

He calls for the ball to be passed to him,
Then flicks it in the air
And on to his chin,
He runs up the pitch,
Doing double time,
When their ape-like defender shouts,
"Leave him to me, he's mine"
The defender dived at Lee,
Trying his luck,
But Lee quickly sidestepped him,
Leaving him sprawled out in the muck;
Lee then let the ball drop,
On to his toe,
He sidestepped the goalie

Then let the ball go,
The ball screamed through
The air and into the net,
The crowd shouted "Goal!"
But Lee wasn't finished yet;
Another six goals
He scored on that day,
So you see in future
Glen Hoddle says, for England Lee shall play.

It's Raining

Outside it's raining,
So I can't play out,
But I like the rain,
I like to splash about;
I put on my mac,
My scarf and my wellies,
Then I jump up and down on slugs
And squash their big fat bellies.

Rinky Tinky

Rinky Tinky, our doggy did a stinky,
Just behind the kitchen door;
He said to the cat,
"What do you think about that?
And if you like I'll do a little bit more!"

I Like

Jilly she likes riding,
Emma she has skates,
Debbie she likes swimming,
and Julie has her paints,
Mandy she likes singing,
And Carol has her clothes,
Me, I don't like anything,
Except picking my big nose.

Love Letter

I sent Susan a letter,
Saying how I feel,
I told her that I love her,
And that my love was real,
I said that if she loves me,
She only has to say:
But she sent me back my letter,
Saying, "Just go away!"

Needles

I fell down in the playground,
And cut my knee so deep,
I had to go to hospital,
So I had a little weep,
It's the thought of being sewn up,
Using needle and thread,
That sends shivers down my spine,
And fills me full of dread,
You see, I don't like needles,
Of any shape and size,
And getting sewn up like an old sock,
Just brings tears to my eyes;
So I think that I will be brave,
And try not to scream and shout,
But I think that when I see the needle,
I will probably just pass out.

Grass of the Class

Watch out kids, here he comes,
It's Tunnel Mouth Timmins
With his flapping gums,
He's the grass of the class,
A loaded windbag filled with gas.

We call him Tunnel Mouth
But his real name is Rob,
We just call him Tunnel Mouth
Because he has a very big gob,
He's the grass of the class,
A loaded windbag filled with gas.

He likes to tell tales,
Just to get people in trouble,
No one tells him their secrets,
They just get out of his way, on the double,
Yes, he's the grass of the class,
A loaded windbag filled with gas

Tunnel mouth Timmins
Has no friends,
He even drives his teachers
Round the bend,
With his "Miss, he said this"
And "Miss, he said that"
He's an annoying creep,
A very spoilt brat,
That's the grass of the class,
A loaded windbag filled with gas

Little Fly

Little fly floating in the air,
Buzzing round without a care,
Landing on cowpats,
And having a suck,
|Then landing on my sandwich,
Your feet covered in muck,
Then you jump onto my doughnut,
And have a good sneeze,
From your snout pours a strange snot,
Full of disease;
So, little fly, as you pass on your germs,
There is just one thing that you must learn;
That is, don't land near me,
So matter of fact,
Because I will hit you with a rolled-up paper,
And you will go "Splat!"

Cheesy Feet

My dad's feet give off
A cheesy sort of smell,
And just what causes this
We really cannot tell,
Could it be his socks,
Or maybe his shoes,
We have to wear a gasmask,
When they are both removed.
He's tried putting on talc,
And leaving his feet to breathe,
He's sprayed them with deoderant,
But they still smell of cheese,
My dad's tried out everything,
The chemist has to sell,
To cut out that pong,
And stop that cheesy smell,
So there was just one thing
Left for us to do
That was to make dad
Keep on his socks and shoes
"I don't want to smell your feet "
My mother said,
"So you can keep your shoes on,
Even when in bed"
So our house doesn't smell
Of cheese no more,
And if dad changes his socks,
It's outside the back door.

My Goldfish

If my goldfish could talk
I wonder what he would say
Would it be that I were wonderful
Or maybe just OK
Would he say
"I like my new fish bowl"
Or would he rather be swimming in a shoal
Would he say that he loves me
And ask for a hug
Or would he just stare with those
Fishy eyes and just say "Glug!"

The Jungle Room

I arrived home from school,
To find all my clothes in bundles,
My mum had had an habdab,
Saying my room was like a jungle,
What could she mean,
By such a remark,
There's no trees or animals in there,
But there is a few furry curry marks;
She says there is bits of old food,
And old sweaty socks,
She's even found a dead mouse,
In an old box

I told her that it's not a dead mouse,
But my old pet gerbil,
And I placed him in the box,
But then I forgot to do the burial.
Then she asked how the curry stains
Had got on to my door
I explained it got splattered,
When I tripped over my trainers,
That lay hidden on the floor;
And I thought that to leave a
Few stains would be for the best,
So I could study the mould for
A forthcoming biology test,
Mum says that in future
I must keep my room clean,
I suppose I would do anything,
Rather than listen to her scream

Hickory Dickory Spock

Hickory Dickory Dock,
Captain Kirk is to marry Mr Spock.
But Mr Spock's mum
Thought it odd of her son,
When she saw him in a wedding frock.

Watch where you're going

I was not looking at the road,
While riding my bike;
I was not obeying any signs,
I just did as I liked.
When it just happened,
Although I had not gone far,
I didn't notice that behind me was
A speeding car.
So I just pulled out,
Without looking back,
The car hit my bike
With a mighty smack;
All that I remember
Is flying through the air,
The next thing I remember
Was waking in intensive care.
The doctors they say
I have damaged my spine,
And for me to walk again
Will take a long time,
So I would just like to say,
That if you are out on the road,
Always look around you
And please remember the highway code!

Sir Albert and His Dragon

In days of old,
When knights were bold,
And dragons were such pests,
There was an old knight called Sir Albert,
Who wore and old string vest.
Now Sir Albert was a strange sight,
With a crooked sword around his hips,
He didn't much like killing dragons,
But he loved munching on fish and chips.
Then one day while walking,
All alone out in the glen,
Albert came across a dragon,
That had eaten thirty men;
But Albert did not panic,
He just gave a toothless grin,
Then offered the dragon fish and chips
Saying, "Here, get stuck in"
So the dragon ate Albert's supper,
He burped, and then he grinned,
Saying "Any chance of any more,
Because eating humans gives me wind."
So Sir Albert struck up a friendship,
With this mighty beast
Every night they would settle down
And on fish and chips would feast;

So it is said by travellers,
Who talk through quiet hushed lips,
Of seeing a dragon and a string-vested knight
Dining on fish and chips.

Night Time Sky

Every night I lay on my bed,
And I stare up at the stars,
I often wonder which one is Venus,
And if it's close to Mars.
You see, I don't know anything
About the night time sky,
But in between the planets,
I know I would like to fly;
I would wave at all the martians,
Who live in great canals,
And I would bring some moon rock,
Just to show to all my pals.
So I hope that, one day,
I can fly to outer space,
Exploring planets new,
And making friends with an alien race;
So, until the day,
I'll just lay here on my bed,
Staring at the stars,
With all my adventures in my head.

Bullied

She lies crying in her bedroom,
All alone.
She does this every evening
When she gets home.
I wonder what could it be
That could make such a young girl cry?
Who could make her so sad
That she wishes she could die?
The problem was the other kids at school
Who hit her and called her a fool.
She has no friends,
And nowhere to turn.
She goes to school,
But is too frightened to learn.

All she needs is just one friend,
Someone to talk to,
To help the misery end.
Do you know this girl?
Does she sit next to you?
Would you offer her your hand in friendship,
Or are you just a bully too?

Author's Note

These poems were written to help my son, Lee, with his reading and writing. The poems are written in a simple style and the content is very much that of "playground humour".

After many readings in schools in West Yorkshire I have found that, as with my son, this basic style and humour encourages children who might not be keen on writing, for whatever reason, to at least have a go. I think it's a case of "If this idiot can do it then so can I".

My son, who is now ten years old at the time of going to press, writes poems of his own, something he would never have done a year ago. So, even though this book is not a poetic masterpiece, children do find it very very funny, and if it encourages just one child to pick up another book and carry on reading, then it will have been worth becoming "Mr Spot on the Bum".

Gez Walsh

Acknowledgements

Thanks to Debbie Nunn, Steve Rudd, Terry Sorfleet and Phillip Rendell, for their hard work and faith, without which this book would not exist. Thanks also to Julie Thompson for her brilliant drawings which bring the poems to life, and to Ian McMillan for his foreword. Last, but not least, thanks to my wife Carol and son Lee for just smiling when people call out "I've Got a Spot on My Bum" to them in the street.